JAZZ PIANO SCALES

GRADES 1–5

The Associated Board of the Royal Schools of Music

Introduction

All good jazz sounds effortless, but that sense of ease is usually achieved through regular hard work and the skills developed by the practice of scales and arpeggios. Learnt in the right way, scales and arpeggios really *can* create new opportunities, enabling you to do more and be more imaginative.

The scales in the jazz piano syllabus have been organized progressively to develop the technical control, flexibility and knowledge of the geography of the keyboard (i.e. where the sharps and flats are) needed in improvised performance. They'll also familiarize you in a systematic way with the common patterns, roots and key centres found in jazz. You'll play patterns like pentatonic and blues scales and various modes, and over the grades you'll build up a variety of these patterns on common roots, like C, F and G. You'll also find that at different grades different *keys* are emphasized: at Grade 1, for example, C major, major pentatonic on C, Mixolydian on G and Dorian on D are all related to the key centre of C. Working through this structure systematically will help you broaden the musical choices you can make as you improvise. (For full details on the rationale of the scale syllabus, read the chapter 'Scales, Arpeggios and Broken Chords' in *Jazz Piano from Scratch*, published by the Board.)

Fingering

The fingerings given are not obligatory; many of these patterns can be fingered in any number of ways. In the exam you'll be assessed on the accuracy and fluency of the scale played, rather than on how it is fingered — if it sounds musical it will probably pass. Remember, though, that poor and inconsistent fingering often leads to a second-rate musical result.

At the same time, the fingerings given have been carefully chosen to prepare you for the most common chord sequences and melodic phrases. In a number of cases alternative fingerings are provided; if you learn these different fingerings, you'll find in performance that you can choose the one which suits the improvisation context best.

Practice routines

In the few weeks before an exam it's a good idea to practise your scales and arpeggios as you'll play them before the examiner. But there are lots of other ways to practise scales, and up to this point they should instead be practised more as they would be used in the performance of a piece.

The chapter on scales in *Jazz Piano from Scratch* gives some helpful advice on different musical ways to practise scales. In short, be more flexible when practising, for example, starting on different notes of the scale, changing direction at random, using a variety of rhythms, including swing and straight feels, and experimenting with different shapes, dynamics and articulation. You are also strongly advised to integrate improvisation with scale practice by improvising wherever possible.

Listen carefully to your own playing, in order to become aware of those aspects of your technique you need to work on, and then devise suitable strategies to improve these aspects. Use the practice routines suggested as starting-points to develop your technique.

The Exam

In the exam you need to play the scales and arpeggios from memory. The examiner will normally ask for at least one pattern from each type of scale, arpeggio or broken chord required at that grade, and from Grade 1 can ask for the patterns to be played in swing or straight 8s.

Examiners will be looking for the following qualities in your playing of the technical requirements:

- accurate and fluent realization from memory of the patterns set for the grade
- even tone across all five fingers of both hands
- independence of the fingers
- an even and positive sense of pulse and rhythm
- a knowledge of the geography of the keyboard
- smooth negotiation of common technical problems, for example, putting the thumb underneath, dealing with awkward leaps, running out of fingers, etc.

Speeds

The table below gives the recommended *minimum* speeds for the playing of the technical requirements at the different grades:

grade	*scales*	*arpeggios and broken chords*
1	♩ = 60	♩ = 46
2	♩ = 66	♩ = 63
3	♩ = 80	♩ = 69
4	𝅗𝅥 = 52	♩ = 76
5	𝅗𝅥 = 63	♩ = 88

Finally, remember that the discipline of practising scales and arpeggios *does* lead to freer, more expressive playing in the end. It really *is* worth the effort!

Charles Beale

GRADE 1

Scales

with each hand separately, straight or swing

DORIAN 2 Octaves
on D

MIXOLYDIAN 2 Octaves
on G

C MAJOR 2 Octaves

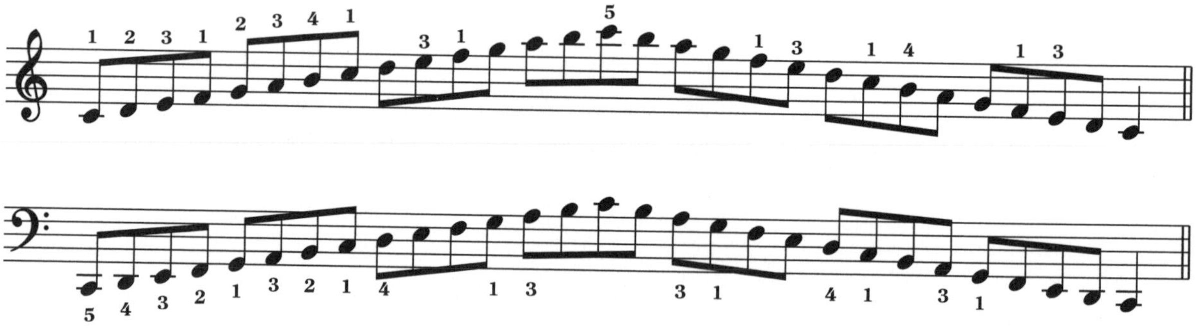

MAJOR PENTATONIC
on C five notes

GRADE 1

♭3 PENTATONIC on G five notes

Arpeggios
with each hand separately, straight or swing

G MAJOR 1 Octave

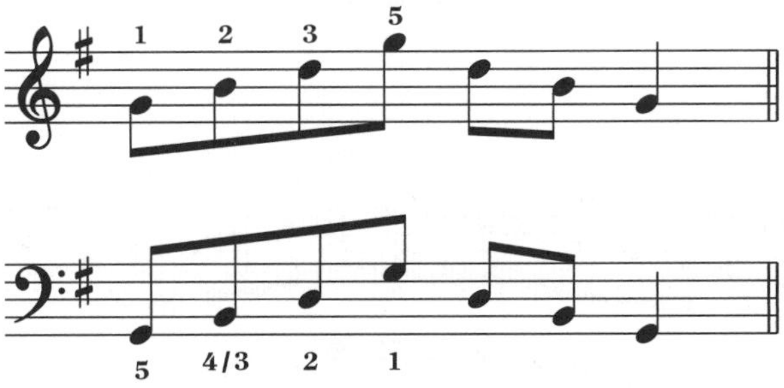

D MINOR 1 Octave

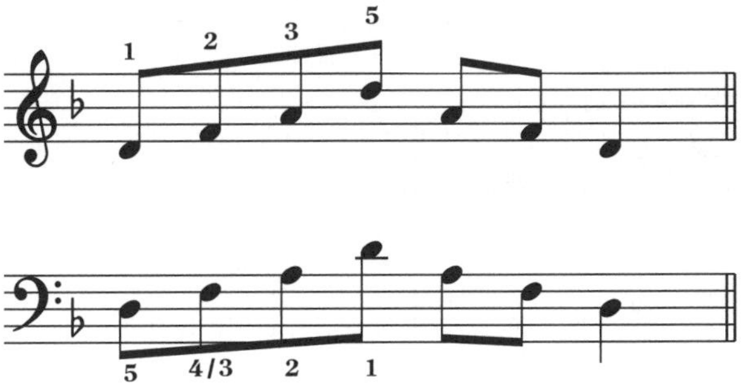

GRADE 2

Scales

with hands together one octave apart, and with each hand separately, straight or swing

DORIAN 2 Octaves
on A

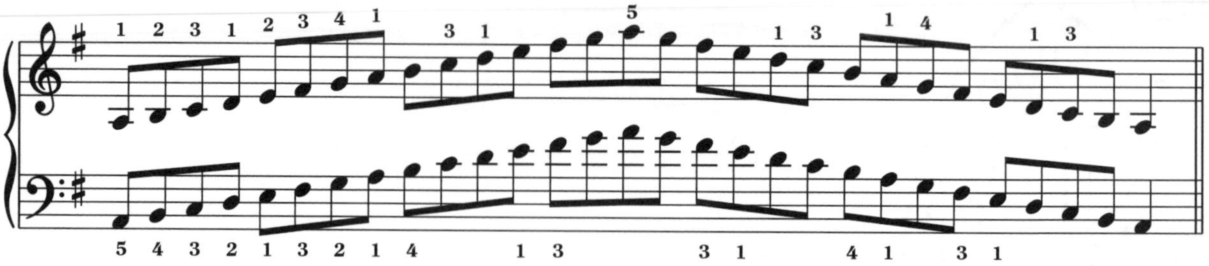

MIXOLYDIAN 2 Octaves
on D

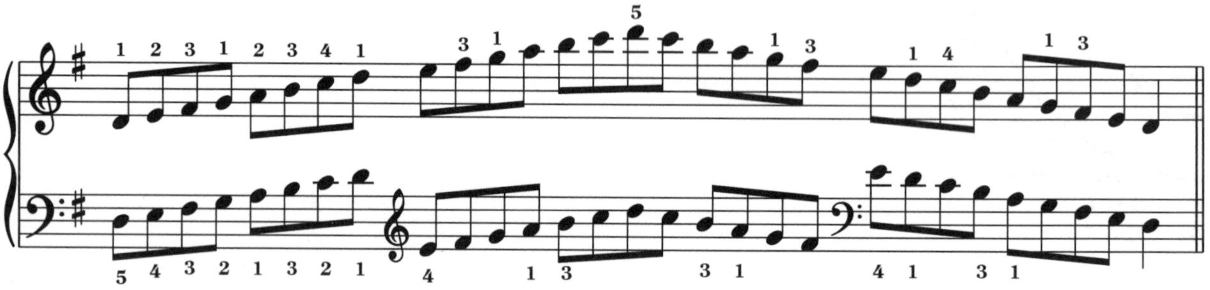

G MAJOR 2 Octaves

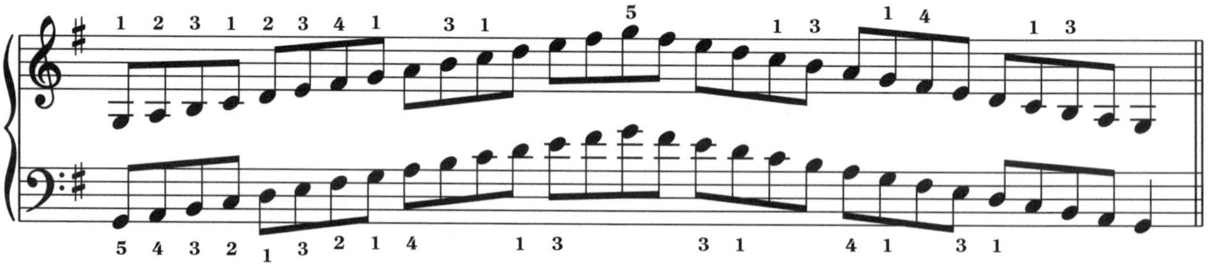

MAJOR PENTATONIC
on F five notes

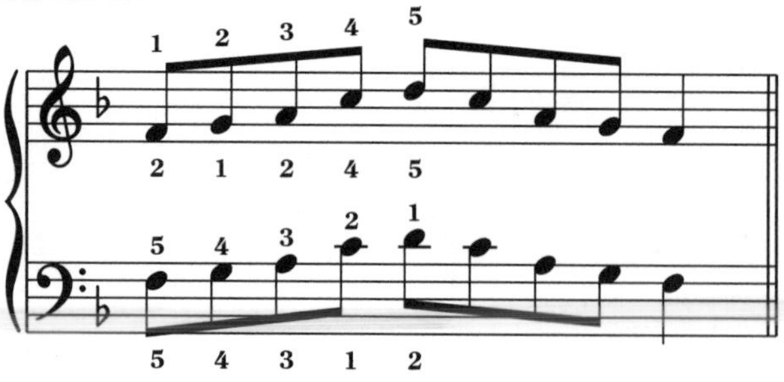

♭3 PENTATONIC
on C five notes

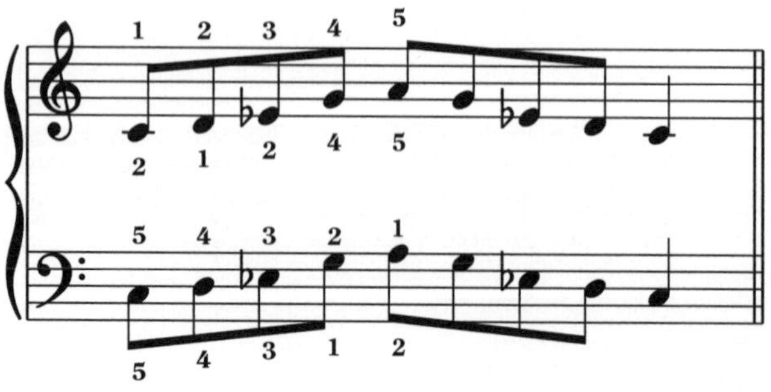

GRADE 2

MINOR PENTATONIC
on A five notes

BLUES SCALE
on D 1 Octave

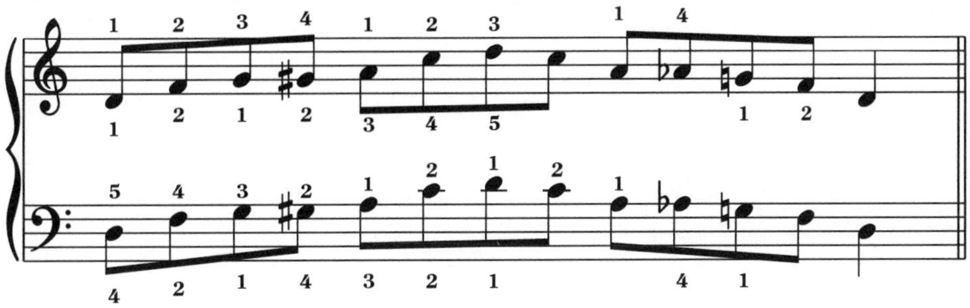

Chromatic scale
with each hand separately, straight or swing

on D 1 Octave

Arpeggios
with each hand separately, straight or swing

D MAJOR 2 Octaves

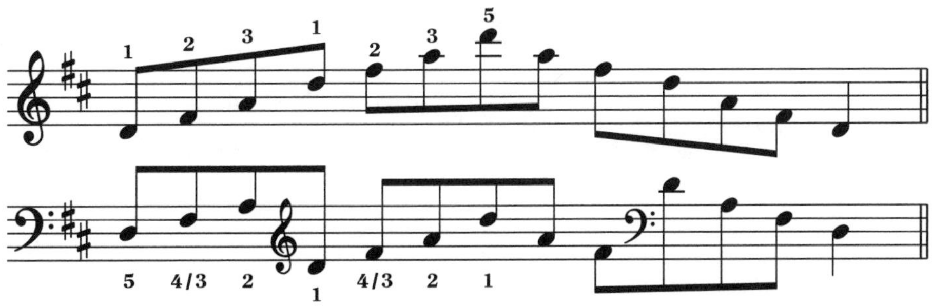

G MINOR 2 Octaves

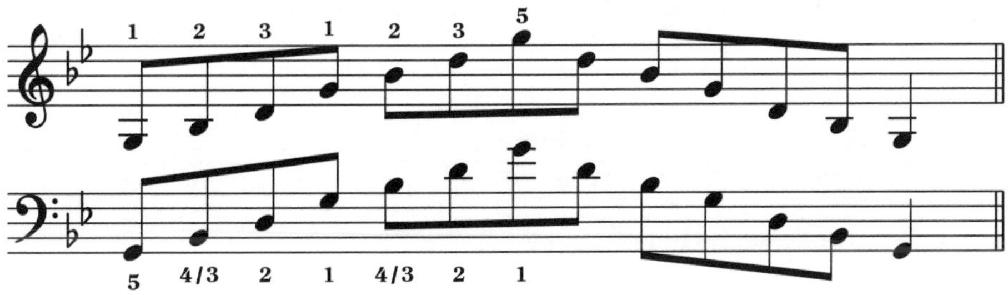

GRADE 3

Scales

with hands together one octave apart, and with each hand separately, straight or swing

DORIAN 2 Octaves
on G

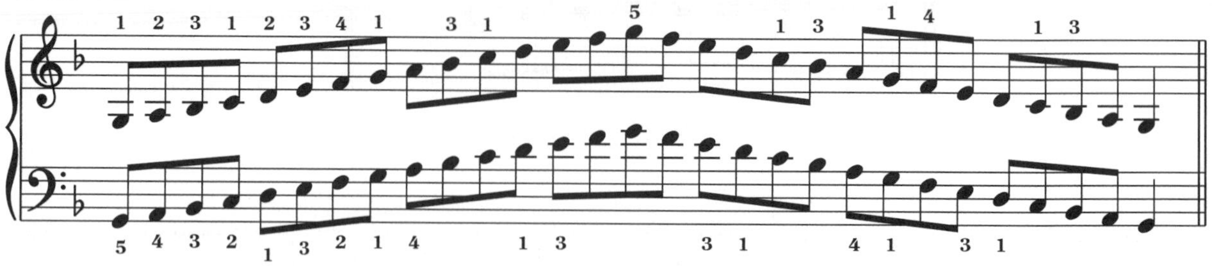

MIXOLYDIAN 2 Octaves
on C

LYDIAN 2 Octaves
on B♭

F MAJOR 2 Octaves

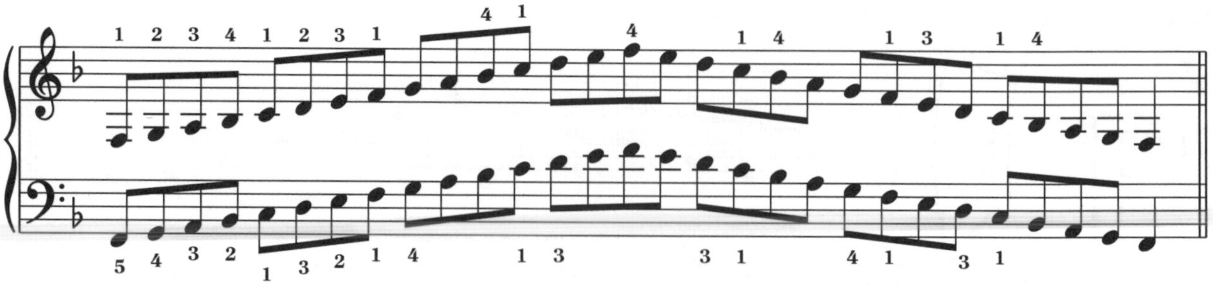

MINOR PENTATONIC
on D 2 Octaves

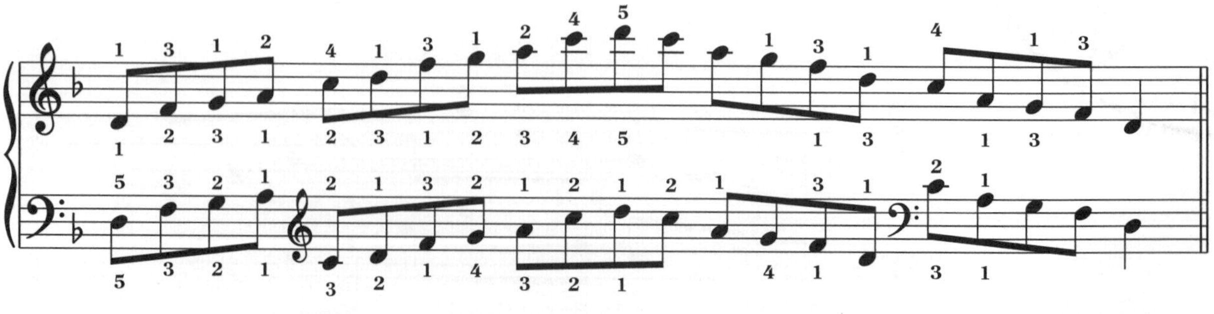

GRADE 3

MINOR PENTATONIC
on C 2 Octaves

BLUES SCALE
on C 1 Octave

BLUES SCALE
on F 1 Octave

Chromatic scales

with each hand separately (fingering for second octave as given below), straight or swing

on A♭ 2 Octaves

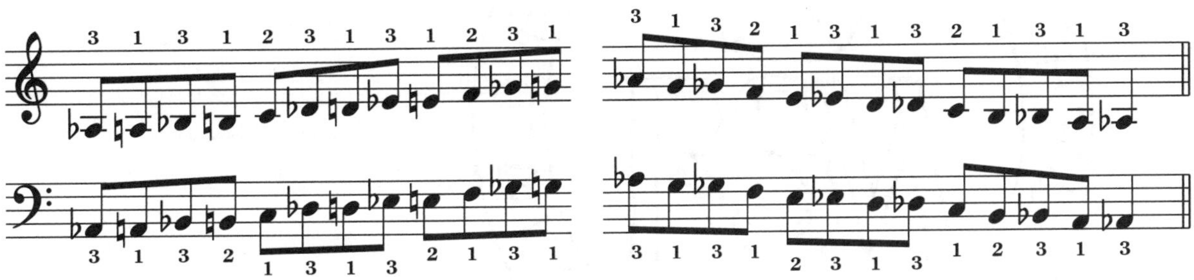

on B 2 Octaves

GRADE 3

on C 2 Octaves

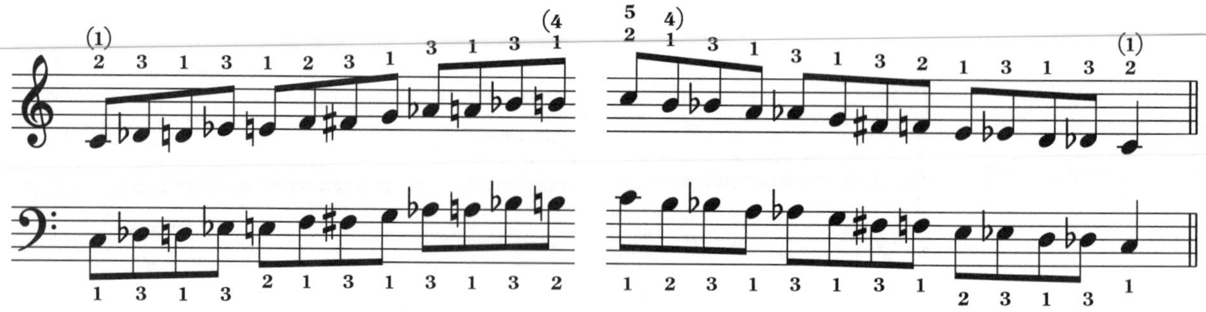

Arpeggios
with each hand separately, straight or swing

F MAJOR 2 Octaves

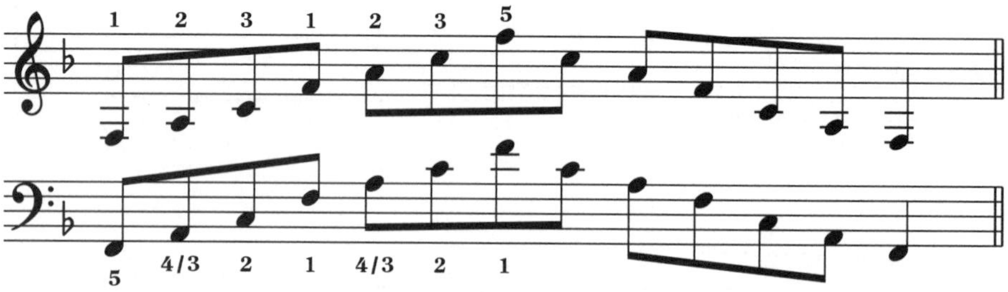

B♭ MAJOR 2 Octaves

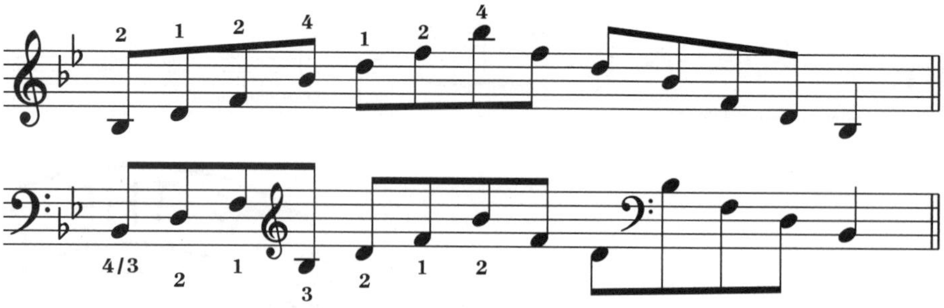

A MINOR 2 Octaves

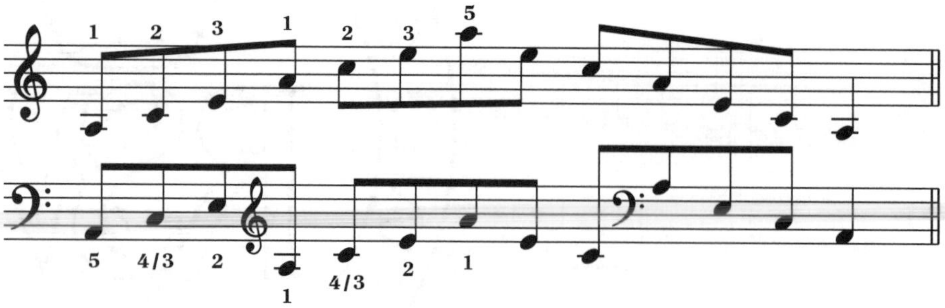

C MINOR 2 Octaves

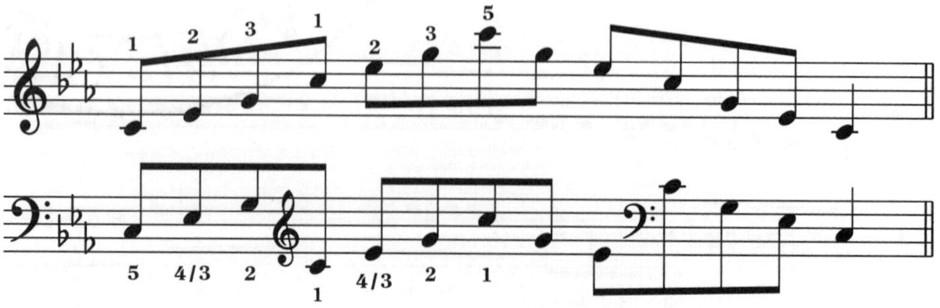

GRADE 4

Scales

with hands together one octave apart, and with each hand separately, straight or swing

DORIAN 2 Octaves
on E

DORIAN 2 Octaves
on C

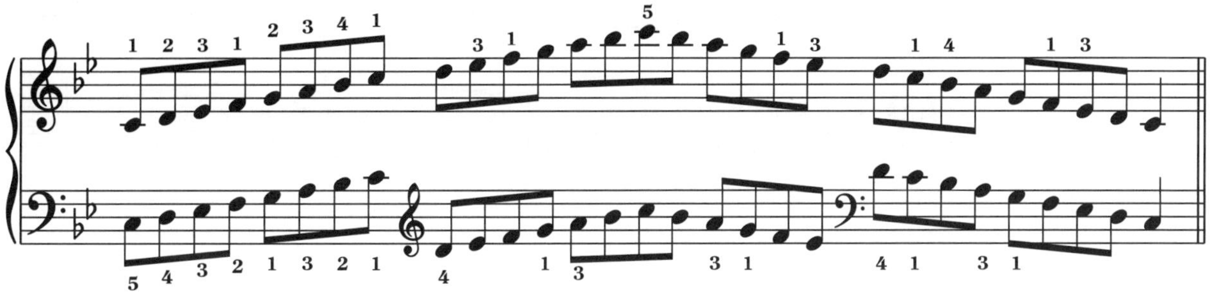

MIXOLYDIAN 2 Octaves
on A

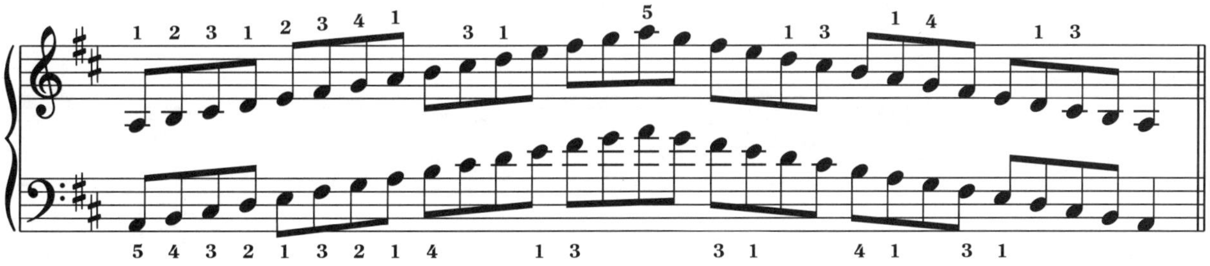

MIXOLYDIAN 2 Octaves
on F

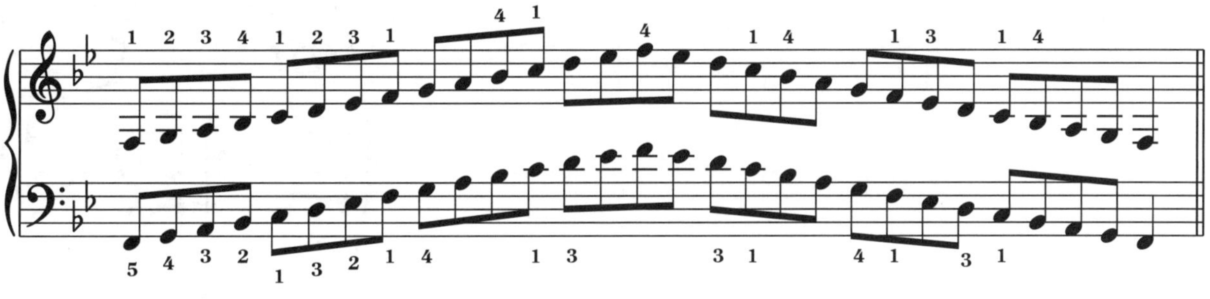

LYDIAN 2 Octaves
on G

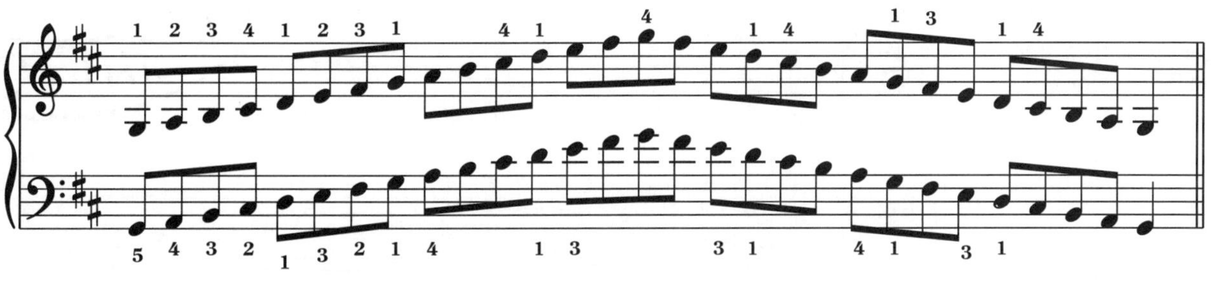

GRADE 4

LYDIAN 2 Octaves
on E♭

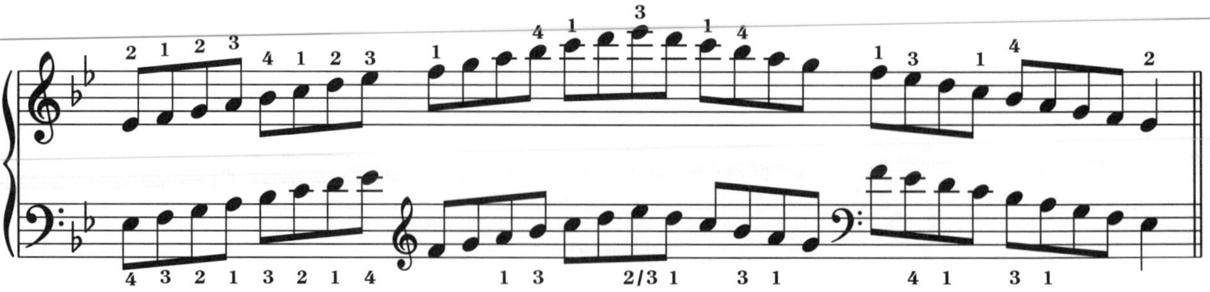

D MAJOR 2 Octaves

B♭ MAJOR 2 Octaves

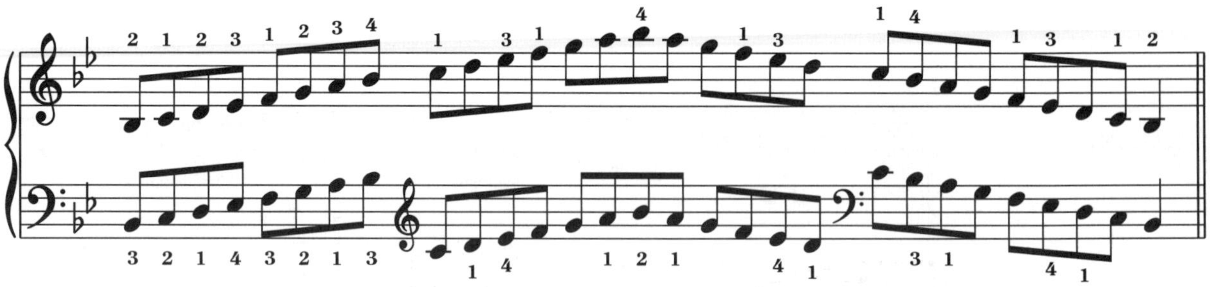

MAJOR PENTATONIC
on G 2 Octaves

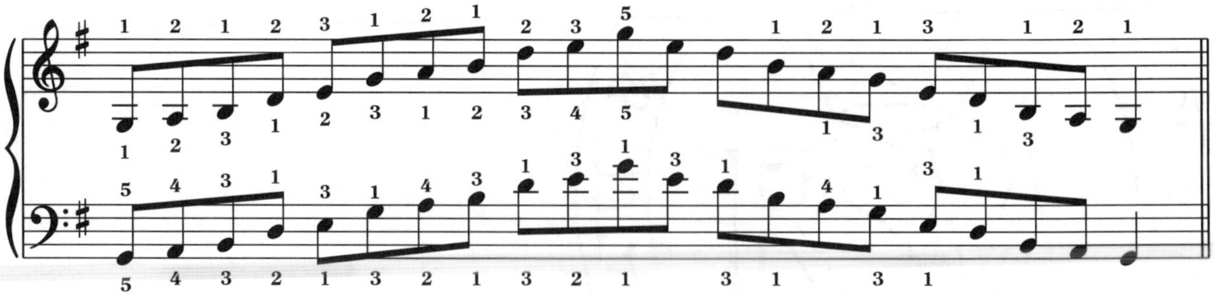

MAJOR PENTATONIC
on E♭ 2 Octaves

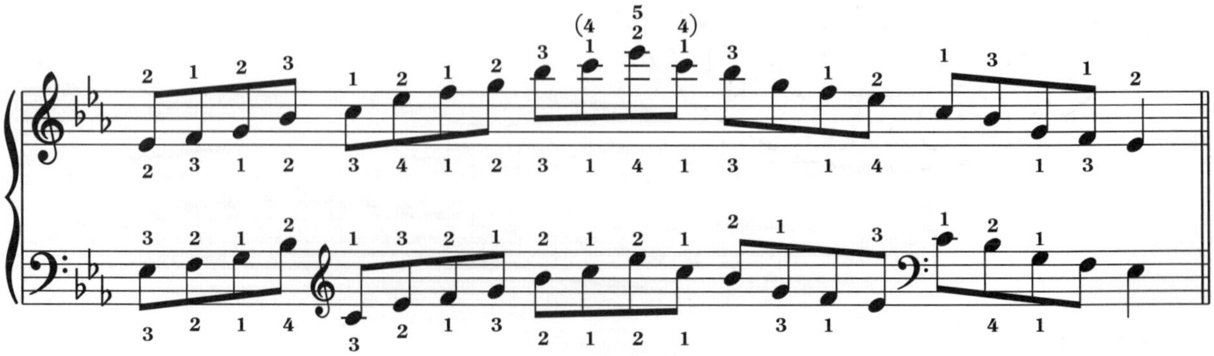

GRADE 4

MINOR PENTATONIC on E 2 Octaves

BLUES SCALE on B♭ 1 Octave

BLUES SCALE on E 1 Octave

Chromatic scales

with hands together one octave apart, and with each hand separately, beginning on any black key named by the examiner, straight or swing

this example is a guide

On any black key 2 Octaves

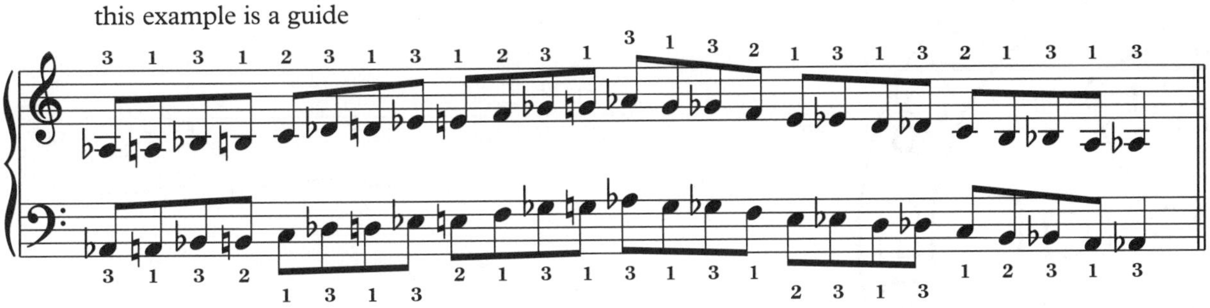

Arpeggios

with hands together one octave apart, and with each hand separately, straight or swing

A MAJOR 2 Octaves

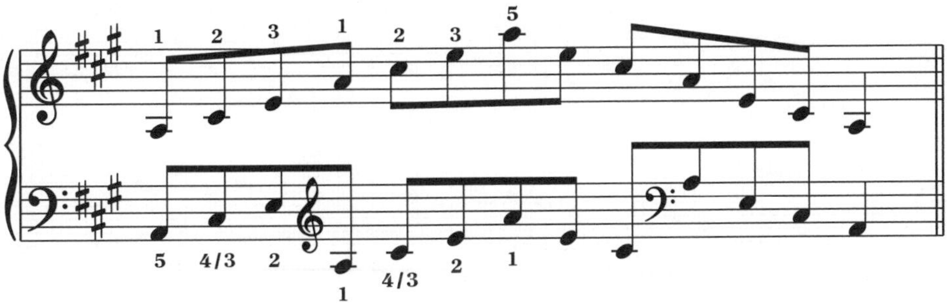

GRADE 4

E♭ MAJOR 2 Octaves

Broken chords
with each hand separately, straight or swing

C7

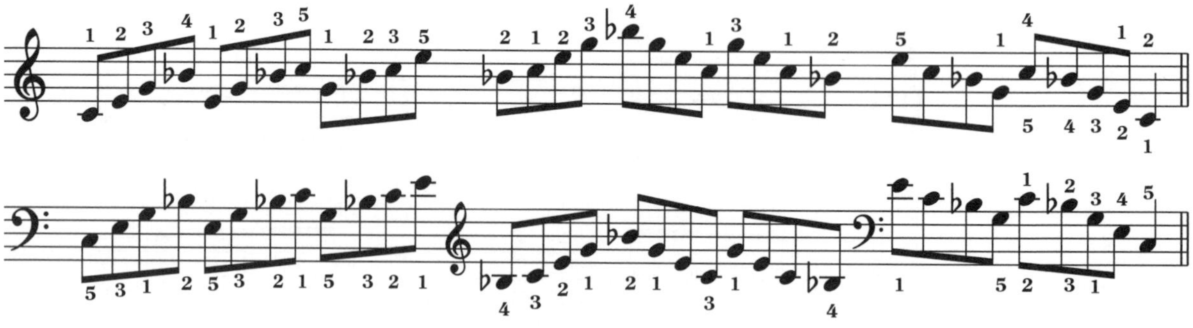

G7

Am7

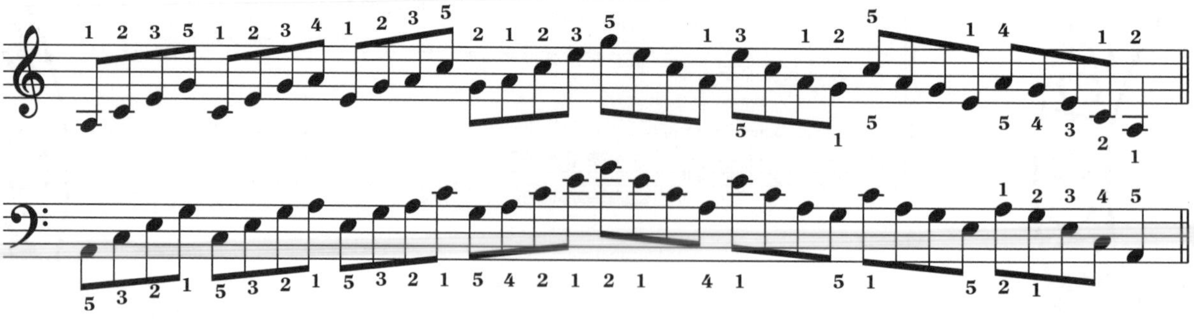

Gm7

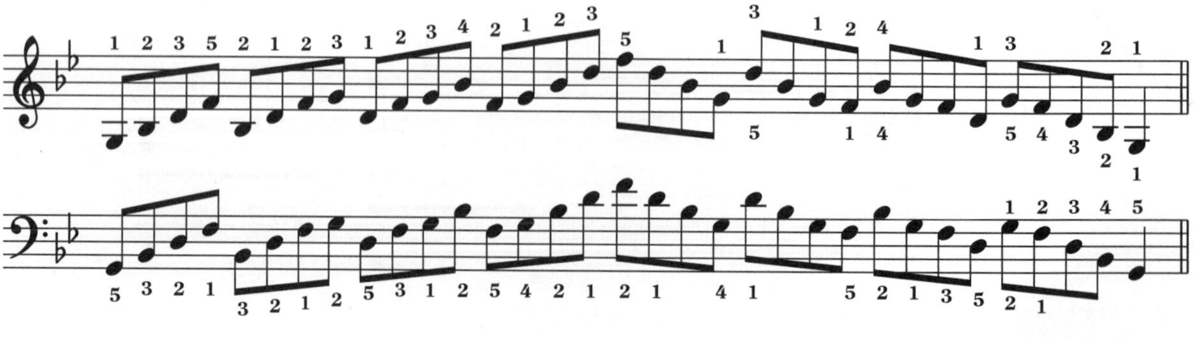

GRADE 5

Scales

with hands together one octave apart, and with each hand separately, straight or swing

DORIAN 2 Octaves
on B

DORIAN 2 Octaves
on F

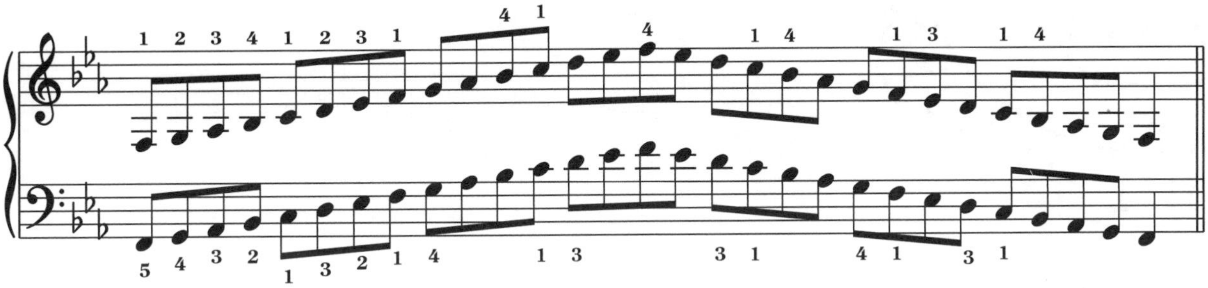

MIXOLYDIAN 2 Octaves
on E

MIXOLYDIAN 2 Octaves
on B♭

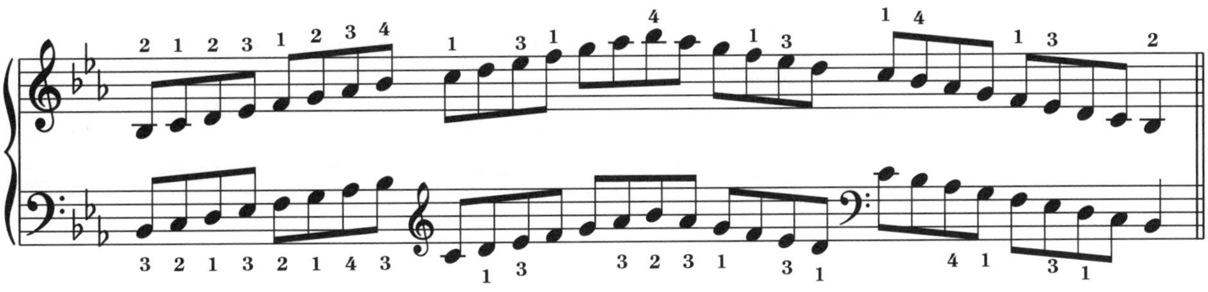

LYDIAN 2 Octaves
on F

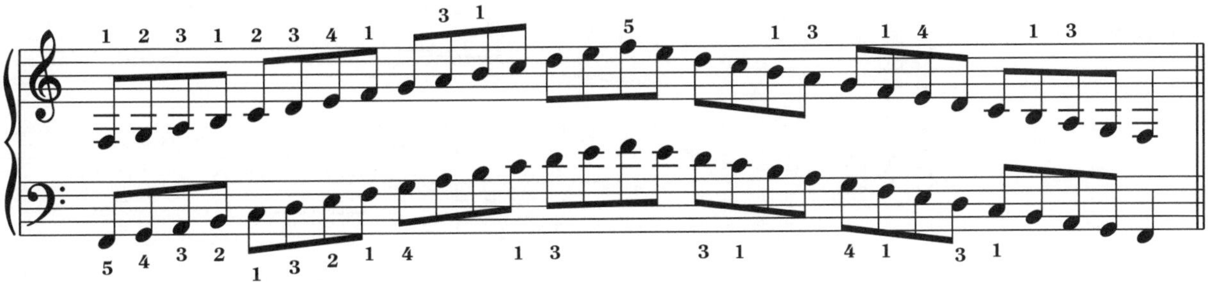

GRADE 5

LYDIAN on C 2 Octaves

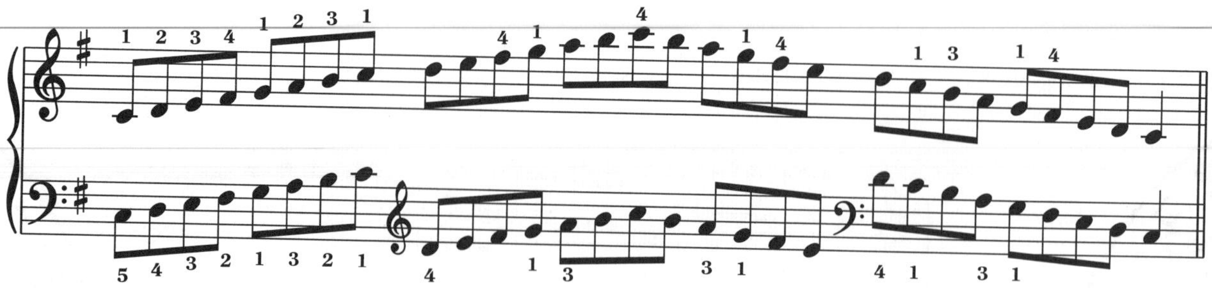

LYDIAN on D 2 Octaves

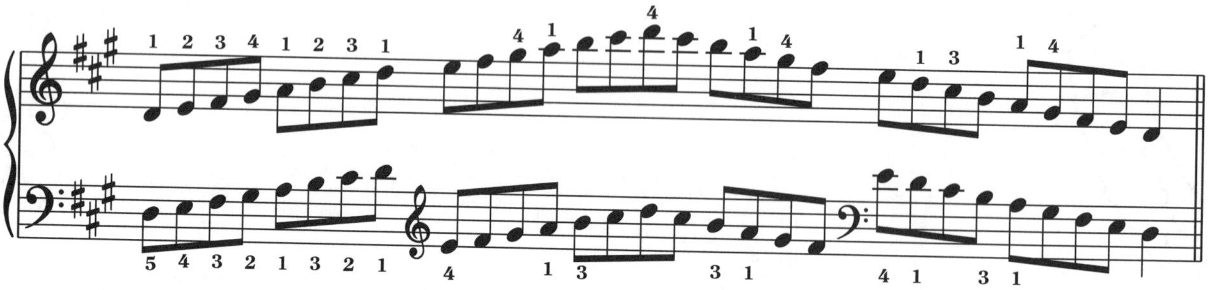

LYDIAN on A♭ 2 Octaves

A MAJOR 2 Octaves

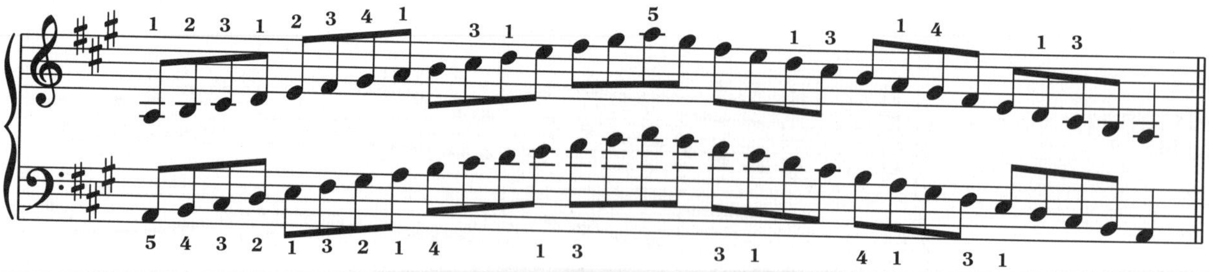

E♭ MAJOR 2 Octaves

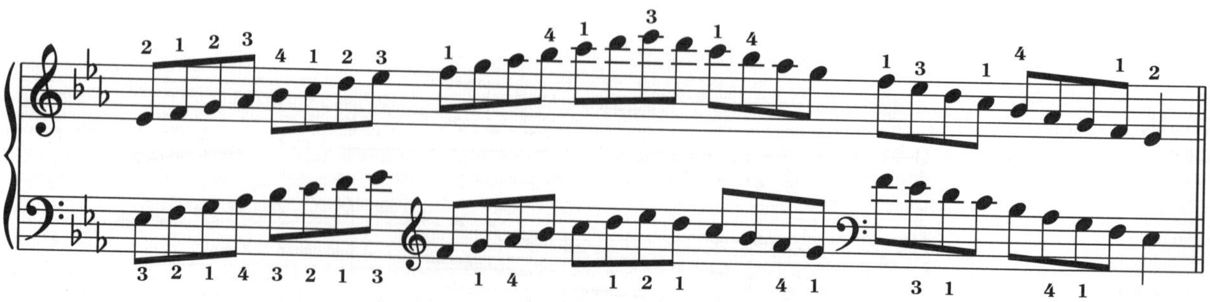

GRADE 5

MAJOR PENTATONIC on D 2 Octaves

MAJOR PENTATONIC on B♭ 2 Octaves

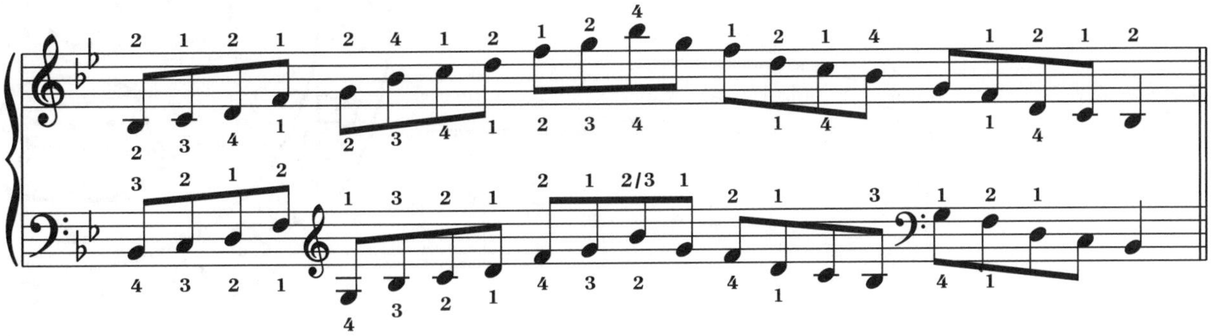

MINOR PENTATONIC on B 2 Octaves

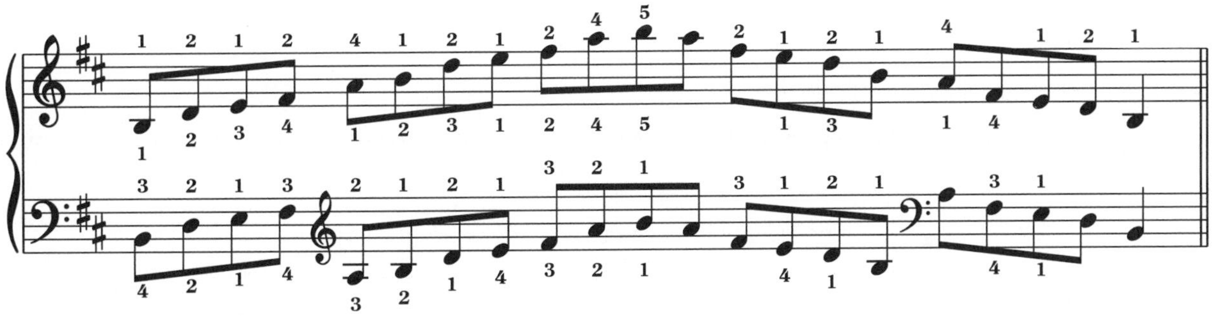

MINOR PENTATONIC on G 2 Octaves

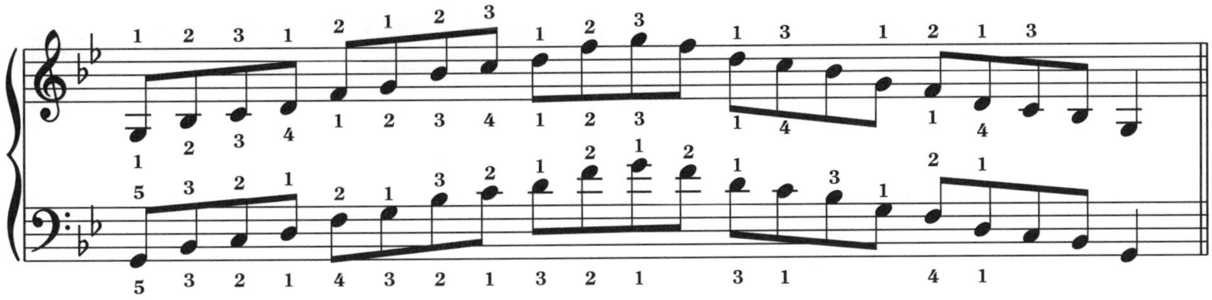

BLUES SCALE on A 1 Octave

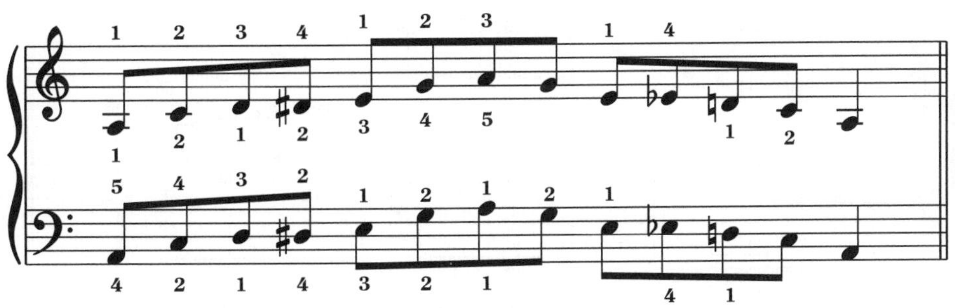

GRADE 5

BLUES SCALE on F# 1 Octave

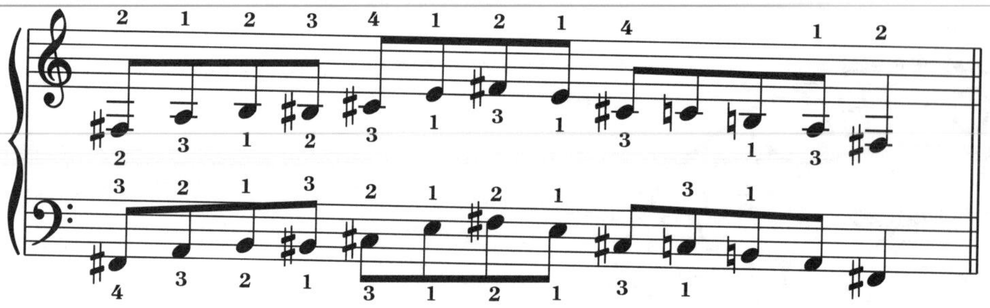

BLUES SCALE on G 1 Octave

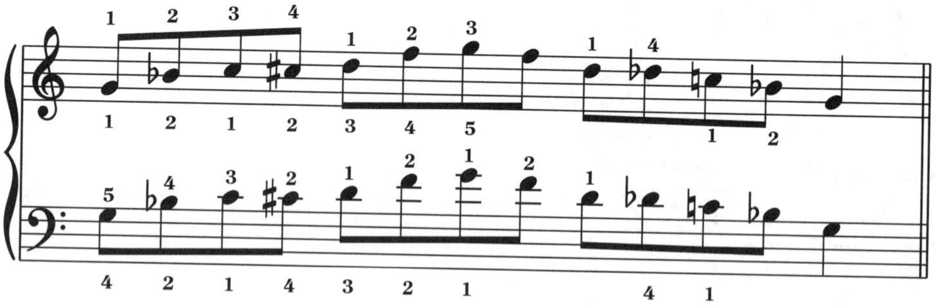

Chromatic scales

with hands together one octave apart, and with each hand separately, beginning on any note named by the examiner, straight or swing

On any note 2 Octaves

this example is a guide

Arpeggios

with hands together one octave apart, and with each hand separately, straight or swing

E MAJOR 2 Octaves

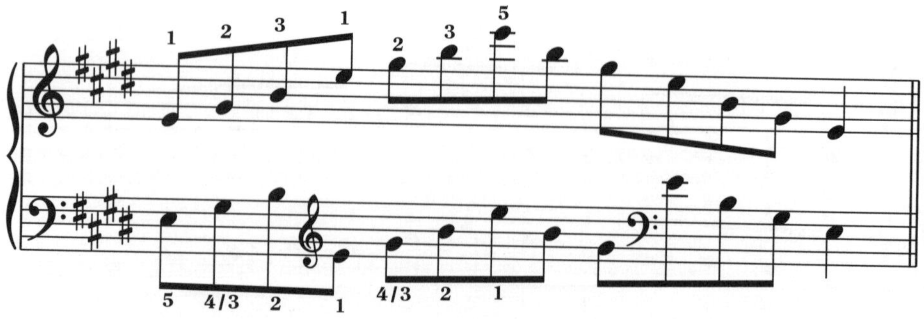

GRADE 5

A♭ MAJOR 2 Octaves

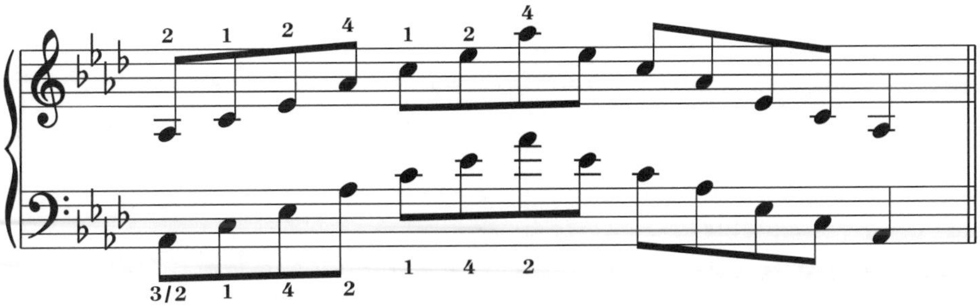

F# MINOR 2 Octaves

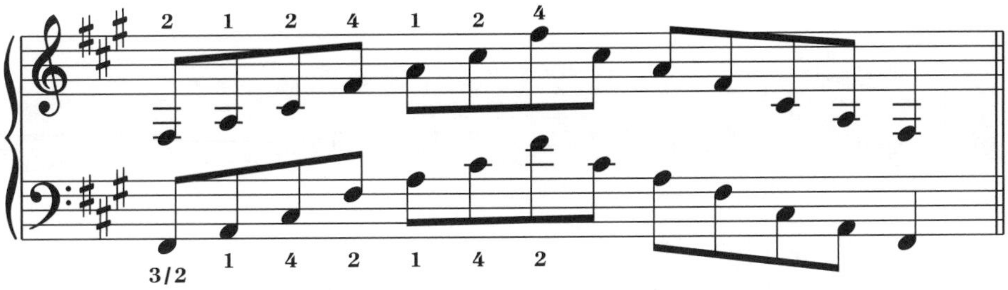

F MINOR 2 Octaves

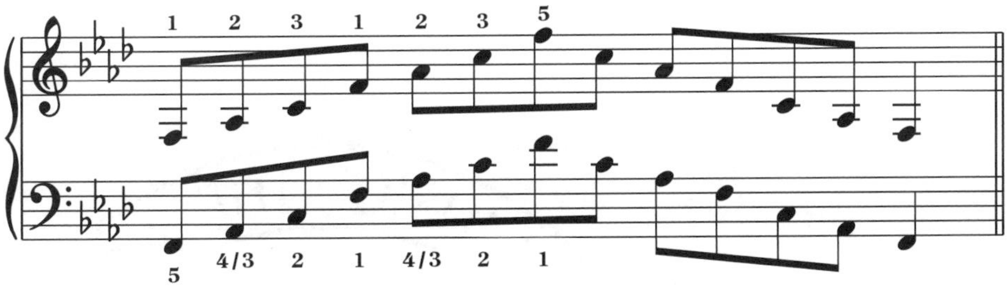

Broken chords

with each hand separately, straight or swing

D7

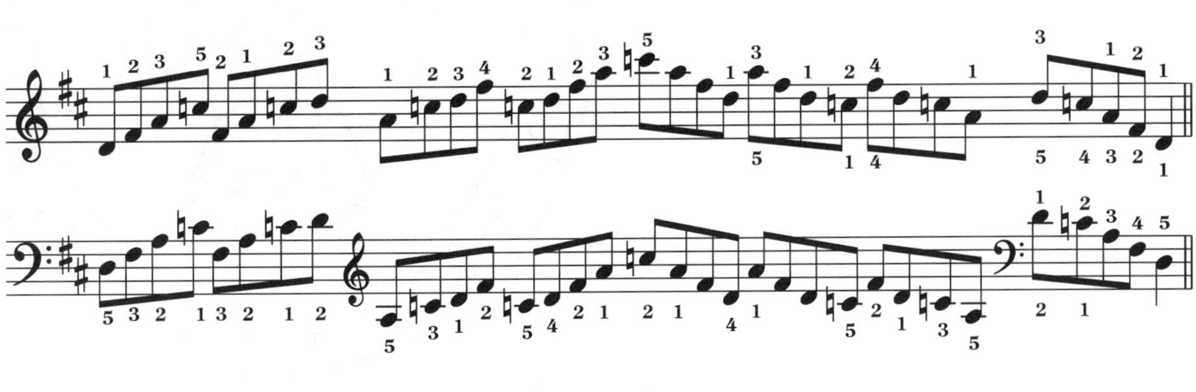

F7

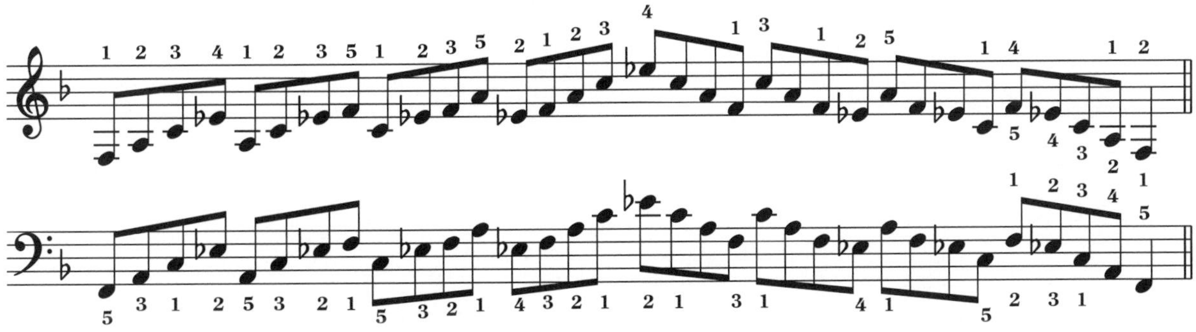

GRADE 5

B♭7

Em7

Bm7

Dm7

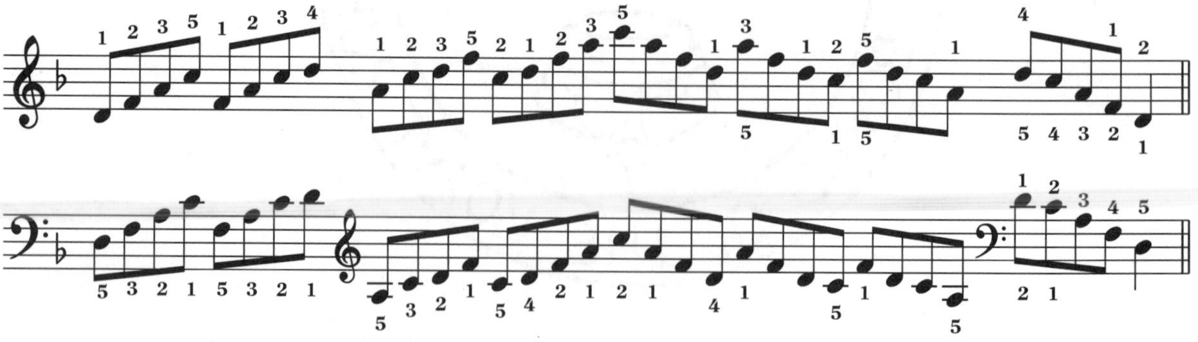

Printed in England by Caligraving Limited Thetford Norfolk

6:98